The Piccolo Book of Cartoons

Also available in Piccolo

by Deborah Manley

Piccolo All the Year Round Book

with Peta Rée

The Piccolo Picnic Book

Piccolo Book of Parties and Party Games

Piccolo Book of Games for Journeys

with Peta Rée and Margaret Murphy

The Piccolo Holiday Book

with Pamela Cotterill

Maps and Map Games

The Piccolo
Book of Cartoons

compiled by Deborah and Roy Manley

cover illustration by David Bull

Piccolo Original Pan Books London and Sydney

First published 1977 by Pan Books Ltd,
Cavaye Place, London SW10 9PG
© Deborah and Roy Manley 1977
ISBN 0 330 25128 7
Printed and bound in Great Britain by
Cox & Wyman Ltd, London, Reading and Fakenham

Contents

Acknowledgements

The authors and publisher gratefully acknowledge the following for permission to reproduce copyright cartoons in this book:
London Express News and Feature Services; Syndication International; Dobs and Barry Appleby; Geoffrey Bles Ltd; Leslie Frewin Publishers Ltd; Alex Graham and the London *Daily Mail*; *Punch*; Ronald Searle and Hope Leresche & Steele; Thelwell and Eyre Methuen Ltd.

Babies

I usually hold this one up for the proud father, it's the lightest

Whatever next?

I know he's an infant prodigy, but at least he could read the paper *after* I've gone to work

The couple who dashed in last night
seem to have pulled a fast one

Baby minding

Little monsters

Have you told them about my spots?

Break out

2 Children

"Happy birthday to me! Happy birthday to me! Happy birthday to Susan! Happy birthday to me!"

Beware of the girls
of St Trinian's

But he's quite big now, mother

Yah! April-fo-ol!

. . . And of the Girl Guides

Peewit Patrol!
Where are yooou?

Beware of the boy

Helping hands

Been downstairs all night, Pa —
helping a man to pack for his holidays!

3 Parents

Oh come along dad!

Parents
at bay

HONEYSETT

**Wouldn't it be easier if we let him get into
bed with us?**

You mean to say you called me in from play,
and made me wash my face and hands for THIS ?

. . . And parents routed

For goodness' sake put more
expression into it — I can't tell
Little Red Riding Hood from the wolf!

Need any more holes drilled
in anything?

The Gambols

4 Man's best friend

Why can't you just bury your bones like other dogs?

A difference of opinion

New friends

O.K., I give up — WHAT has twenty legs and barks?

S–PBC–B

Go home, Spot

Strange friends

It's scared stiff of
flies, but it does keep
the relations away

Long-haired layabouts

Ken Pyne

A dog's best friend

I'd like to introduce the
friends you said I could invite for lunch

5 Bad moments

The cat kept playing with the wool

Around the house

Tea-up, darling!

Don't make such a fuss, dear, you're not the first man to cut himself shaving!

Don't look now

Sounds as if we've caught that ruddy mouse at last

Sorry, everyone — false alarm!

Famous last words

Not to worry — I can't swim

I can't find my mouth

Trouble with the boss

No wonder we haven't had a single
customer today — you forgot
to unlock the doors

Trouble with clothes

My glove got caught !

Here, let me see the instructions

Why don't you let him go home and get his glasses, Harry?

Short-sighted

Don't be a tease, Henry, where are you?

6 Chameleons and other animals

Food for thought

Bird food

... thoughtful chap, to put these little menu cards up, so we know what we're eating...

Be prepared

Why do you always bring that
elephant gun when we go out?

Coming home
to roost

Madge, did you buy a raffle ticket at the
agricultural show?

You've overslept again, Henry

Two can play at this game

Primeval Derby Day

Taken in

. . . on the other hand, it does
keep the killer whales away. . .

Comic horrors

That's the Empire State building
over there!

Two's company

7 Food

Wot, shepherd's pie again?

You chaps seen any reindeers pass this way?

A bit tough

Well, it was never much of a parrot at the best of times, Cap'n.!

... The manager wants a word with whoever's doing the chicken sand-wiches!

First serving for dinner

Sorry, it's closed to visitors at feeding time

S—PBC—C

The master's
meat

Alfie don't want any, he's just ate Elsie

In poor taste

I hope we're in time to see them being fed

We're not removing your plaster until you've eaten
all your cabbage!

Everyone to his taste

They certainly seemed to like that madeira cake

Sick joke

I suppose we shouldn't have,
really — they're terribly fattening

8 At work

There's only the usual couple of escapologists left tonight sir

I really must get myself a pair of steps

Professionals and amateurs

I know it's supposed to be a family act, but

The long
and the short of it

Uh-uh! — Seems it's going to
be one of those days!

One of those days

Had a terrible morning, dear . . .
something wrong with a new
treacle-tart we're selling

Fenced in

9 At school

Come along! Try! Here's a golden
opportunity to learn to read

Practice makes perfect

I'll give her practical science.

Learning to read

He's the boss's son. You're to help him with his maths homework!

Young scientists

I think that concludes the chemistry class for today

Old school teachers

Hollowood

Now I want you all to turn very, very gently to page 57, if it's there, and read chapter II, unless it's been obliterated

What *I* choose to wear, Mrs Preston, is neither here nor there. The fact remains that as a pupil your son MUST wear a school uniform!

School report

10
Entertainment

Dear Ardent Fan: Enclosed please find
a lock of my hair as requested . . . !

The left-handed violinist

Shuddup!

Television times

For God's sake, why don't you take him for a walk? He's obviously bored to tears!..

Party time

It was smashin', Mum –
can I have another party tomorrow?

Kitchen folly

It takes
two to tangle

That's the last time I give you dancing lessons!

11 Sport

If you let me come down and watch Match of the Day, I won't tell you the score. . . . !

Cheerio—I always leave 10 minutes early to
avoid the rush

protection

How to time your jumps

TAKE-OFF JUST RIGHT

Man's best friend

THE HUNTING DOG

And another one

THE GUN DOG

Just fishing

And tell him if he does it again I'm going to keep it!

Please can we have our ball back?

Please can we have our referee back

Ancient combat

No, I'm not sure how many points you score for that

In training

**Turn that record player
off—he can't stop!**

12 Beware of the dog

Kill!

Obedience training

. . . as I was saying, he's mar-
vellous at carrying the shopping
home, unless we meet a cat. . .

Guard dog

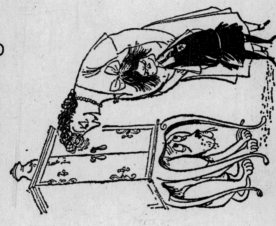

Do come out, Rover, Susan won't bite

13 Transport

Ten minutes we've been away and a ticket already?

Travelling companion

One and a half, please

I wonder why no one else is using this Motorway

On tow

I saw a programme on telly last night about bargees—and their horse walked along the bank!!

Silly boy — it means 'Beware of man having trouble with his umbrella'!

Front seat driver

What a queer sign, Cyril — I wonder what it means?

Last journey

What're you sighing for?

14 Bedtime

You'd better get up—it's time you were getting
ready for bed

The guard dog

While you're up, Fred, get me a glass of water

Water battle

F.J.WINTERBOTTOM

Tail piece

On the next few pages why not draw your own
cartoons or stick in some that you have found